MW00609348

THE BOOK OF John

ONE CHAPTER A DAY

GoodMorningGirls.org

The Book of John

© 2018 Women Living Well Ministries, LLC

ALL RIGHTS RESERVED

No part of this book may be reproduced in any form or by any electronic or mechanical means, including information storage and retrieval systems, without written permission from the author, except in the case of a reviewer, who may quote brief passages embodied in critical articles or in a review.

Scripture is from the ESV® Bible (The Holy Bible, English Standard Version®), copyright © 2001 by Crossway Bibles, a publishing ministry of Good News Publishers. Used by permission. All rights reserved.

Welcome to Good Morning Girls! We are so glad you are joining us.

God created us to walk with Him, to know Him, and to be loved by Him. He is our living well, and when we drink from the water He continually provides, His living water will change the entire course of our lives.

Jesus said: "Whoever drinks of the water that I will give him will never be thirsty again. The water that I will give him will become in him a spring of water welling up to eternal life." ~ John 4:14 (ESV)

So let's begin.

The method we use here at GMG is called the **SOAK** method.

- ❏ **S**—The S stands for *Scripture*—Read the chapter for the day. Then choose 1-2 verses and write them out word for word. (There is no right or wrong choice—just let the Holy Spirit guide you.)

- ❏ **O**—The O stands for *Observation*—Look at the verse or verses you wrote out. Write 1 or 2 observations. What stands out to you? What do you learn about the character of God from these verses? Is there a promise, command or teaching?

- ❏ **A**—The A stands for *Application*—Personalize the verses. What is God saying to you? How can you apply them to your life? Are there any changes you need to make or an action to take?

- ❏ **K**—The K stands for *Kneeling in Prayer*—Pause, kneel and pray. Confess any sin God has revealed to you today. Praise God for His word. Pray the passage over your own life or someone you love. Ask God to help you live out your applications.

SOAK God's word into your heart and squeeze every bit of nourishment you can out of each day's scripture reading. Soon you will find your life transformed by the renewing of your mind!

Walk with the King!

Courtney

WomenLivingWell.org, GoodMorningGirls.org

Join the GMG Community

Share your daily SOAK on **Facebook.com/GoodMorningGirlsWLW**

Instagram: WomenLivingWell #GoodMorningGirls

GMG Bible Coloring Chart

COLORS	KEYWORDS
PURPLE	God, Jesus, Holy Spirit, Saviour, Messiah
PINK	women of the Bible, family, marriage, parenting, friendship, relationships
RED	love, kindness, mercy, compassion, peace, grace
GREEN	faith, obedience, growth, fruit, salvation, fellowship, repentance
YELLOW	worship, prayer, praise, doctrine, angels, miracles,power of God, blessings
BLUE	wisdom, teaching, instruction, commands
ORANGE	prophecy, history, times, places, kings, genealogies, people, numbers, covenants, vows, visions, oaths, future
BROWN/GRAY	Satan, sin, death, hell, evil, idols, false teachers, hypocrisy, temptation

Introduction to the Book of John

I am so excited to begin the book of John with you. John is the fourth gospel in the Bible and it is unlike the previous three gospels. It is unique!

Matthew, Mark and Luke focus on what Jesus taught and did. The book of John focuses on who Jesus is.

- ❏ While the book of Luke shows Jesus in his humanity as the "Son of Man," the book of John shows Jesus in his deity as "The Son of God."

- ❏ The book of John does not start back at the birth of Jesus but rather back at creation revealing the full deity of Jesus.

- ❏ The book of John shows 7 signs and miracles. 6 of these miracles are not mentioned in the other gospels.

- ❏ The book of John includes the seven "I AM" statements. These statements are not included in the other gospels.

- ❏ The book of John records lengthy discussions, discourses and teachings of Jesus and does not include the shorter, proverb-like sayings found in the other gospels.

- ❏ There are almost no parables in the book of John.

Despite all that Jesus revealed to his nation, they did not receive him and instead they crucified him. Jesus laid his life down on the cross and because he is divine, his sacrifice paid the penalty for our sins.

In the book of John, Jesus rose from the dead and walked and talked with his disciples one last time before sending the Holy Spirit.

The Purpose: That we might believe.

John 20:31 says: *"but these are written so that you may believe that Jesus is the Christ, the Son of God, and that by believing you may have life in his name."*

The Author: Although the author is anonymous, tradition holds that John, the beloved disciple, wrote the book of John.

Time Period: This book was written around 90 A.D.

Key Verse: John 1:29

Behold, the Lamb of God, who takes away the sin of the world!

The Outline:

1. Jesus is God in the flesh. (1:1-18)

2. The public ministry of Jesus begins. (1:19-4:54)

3. Jesus performs miracles, gives discourses and faces opposition. (5:1-12:50)

4. Jesus prepares his disciples for the betrayal and says an intercessory prayer. (13:1-17:26)

5. Jesus is arrested, put on trial and crucified. (18:1-19:37)

6. Jesus is buried and resurrects. (19:38-21:25)

God loves us so much that he sent his only son Jesus to die on the cross for our sins and those who believe in him have the assurance of eternal life! Jesus knows our greatest need is Him. He knows our hurts, our struggles, our worries and our fears and he did not leave us alone. He sent the Holy Spirit to comfort us and guide us.

I can't wait to see how God reveals himself personally to each of us as we read the book of John together, chapter by chapter. So let's get started!

Keep walking with the King!

Courtney

The Word became flesh
and dwelt among us,
and we have seen his glory.

John 1:14

Reflection Question:

In John chapter 1, over and over Jesus is referred to as the "Word" and the "light". Jesus and God are one. The Word and the light came into the world in bodily form and they beheld his glory! And then Jesus said to his disciples, "come and see" and "follow me."

Following Jesus is life changing! He is the only light of the world and without him we are left in darkness. How has Jesus changed your life and in what ways is He the light of your life?

S—The S stands for *Scripture*

O—The O stands for *Observation*

A—The A stands for *Application*

K—The K stands for *Kneeling in Prayer*

(Jesus) manifested his glory.

And his disciples believed in him.

John 2:11

Reflection Question:

Notice that the first miracle Jesus ever performed was on the third day of a wedding! This foreshadowed how Jesus revealed his glory, on the third day, when he rose from the dead.

Jesus' disciples already believed in him but their belief was deepened when they saw him turn the water into wine. Tell of a time when God did something great in your life and your belief in him was deepened.

S—The S stands for *Scripture*

O—The O stands for *Observation*

A—The A stands for *Application*

K—The K stands for *Kneeling in Prayer*

He must increase,

but I must decrease.

John 3:30

Reflection Question:

In John 3:29, John says that he rejoices in the voice of the bridegroom and this joy has made him complete. He has determined that Jesus MUST increase and he MUST decrease.

Not only was it vital for John that Jesus increase in his life but it is vital for every believer as well. How can you decrease and Jesus increase more in your life? And how has hearing God's voice brought you joy?

S—The S stands for *Scripture*

O—The O stands for *Observation*

A—The A stands for *Application*

K—The K stands for *Kneeling in Prayer*

Whoever drinks of the water

that I will give him

will never be thirsty again.

John 4:14

Reflection Question:

Jesus offered living water to the woman at the well. This is why I named this ministry—Women Living Well. Women will live well, when they drink from the living well, the living words of God.

Drinking is receiving and it's even easier than eating! So many of us try to fill our needs and inner thirst for meaning, happiness and fulfillment through physical means but there is a spiritual thirst that only Jesus can quench. Think for a moment about your physical thirst and need for water. Do you drink often through out the day? How does this relate to how often you need God's Word through out the day?

John 4

S—The S stands for *Scripture*

O—The O stands for *Observation*

A—The A stands for *Application*

K—The K stands for *Kneeling in Prayer*

*Whoever hears my word
and believes him who sent me
has eternal life.*

John 5:24

Reflection Question:

Whoever hears Jesus' words and believes in God—has eternal life!

This is the gospel! Oh what a wonderful gift it is!

When did you first hear Jesus' words and become a believer? How does it make you feel to know that you will never face judgement and you have received eternal life with God forever in heaven?

S—The S stands for *Scripture*

O—The O stands for *Observation*

A—The A stands for *Application*

K—The K stands for *Kneeling in Prayer*

Jesus said to them,

"I am the bread of life:

whoever comes to me

shall not hunger,

and whoever believes in me

shall never thirst.

John 6:35

Reflection Question:

John chapter 6 is all about bread. First, Jesus feeds the multitudes physical bread and then Jesus shows them that He is their spiritual bread. Jesus said "I am the bread of life." Jesus was showing them that just as bread was necessary for physical life; Jesus is necessary for eternal life.

Many of us turn to food not just because we are hungry but for emotional comfort as well. But what we really need is Jesus. Only he can satisfy the longings of our soul. Are you tempted to turn to other things or other people when your soul is not satisfied? How is Jesus your bread of life?

S—The S stands for *Scripture*

O—The O stands for *Observation*

A—The A stands for *Application*

K—The K stands for *Kneeling in Prayer*

Jesus stood up and cried out,

"If anyone thirsts,

let him come to me and drink."

John 7:37

Reflection Question:

Jesus stood up in the temple courts and shouted out an invitation to all, to come and drink. The word "anyone" is all inclusive—all nations are invited. Jesus even extended this invitation to his enemies. The only qualification was that they must be thirsty.

Jesus' water is free—we simply need to be thirsty and drink. How do you know that your soul is thirsty? And how is Jesus your spring in the midst of your desert?

John 7

S—The S stands for *Scripture*

O—The O stands for *Observation*

A—The A stands for *Application*

K—The K stands for *Kneeling in Prayer*

So if the Son sets you free,

you will be free indeed.

John 8:36

Reflection Question:

Apart from Jesus, we are under Satan's rule and a slave to sin. Satan is a brutal master, a murderer from the beginning and the father of lies. Jesus came to bring us truth and to set us free!

In John 8:31, Jesus said that if we abide in His word, we will know the truth and the truth will set us free. How have you been set free from sin? And how have you been set free to live out the purpose that God has for your life through remaining in God's word?

John 8

S—The S stands for *Scripture*

O—The O stands for *Observation*

A—The A stands for *Application*

K—The K stands for *Kneeling in Prayer*

Jesus answered, "It was not that this man sinned, or his parents, but that the works of God might be displayed in him.

John 9:3

Reflection Question:

Sometimes when we see someone suffering we may think that it is a result of that person's sin. In John 9, the disciples asked Jesus who sinned, the parents or the blind man. Jesus explained that his suffering was not a result of sin but because God had a plan to display his great work through him.

Is there an area in your life—or maybe in the life of a family member or friend - where you have seen suffering and then God did a mighty work through that person and God was glorified? Write what happened below. How does seeing God at work in the midst of suffering encourage you?

S—The S stands for *Scripture*

O—The O stands for *Observation*

A—The A stands for *Application*

K—The K stands for *Kneeling in Prayer*

I came that they may have life

and have it abundantly.

John 10:10

Reflection Question:

When we think about the abundant life, we tend to think of an abundance of possessions but this is not what Jesus was talking about. Our abundant life began the moment we looked to Jesus as our Savior and inherited eternal life in heaven. We have a spiritual abundance that no one can take from us. No thief can steal it. God is always with us.

The Christian's abundant life is one of enjoying the love, peace, grace and truth of our Heavenly Father. He is so very good—even when life is hard, even when our bank accounts are low, and even when life feels mundane. How has God abundantly blessed you inwardly?

S—The S stands for *Scripture*

O—The O stands for *Observation*

A—The A stands for *Application*

K—The K stands for *Kneeling in Prayer*

Jesus said to her,

"I am the resurrection and the life.

Whoever believes in me,

though he die, yet shall he live."

John 11:25

Reflection Question:

Jesus did not just say that he knew about the resurrection and the life but that He *IS* the resurrection and the life. To believe in Jesus is to HAVE resurrection and life!

Jesus is the champion over death! Do you fear death? How does knowing Jesus calm your fears about death?

S—The S stands for *Scripture*

O—The O stands for *Observation*

A—The A stands for *Application*

K—The K stands for *Kneeling in Prayer*

Mary took a pound of expensive ointment

and anointed the feet of Jesus

and wiped his feet with her hair.

John 12:3

Reflection Question:

Mary loved Jesus and her affection toward him was openly lavish, humble and sacrificial. Mary spent nearly a years worth of wages, annointing Jesus' feet with expensive perfume and then wiping his feet with her hair. In contrast to Mary, Judas loved money. Judas betrayed Jesus for just 30 pieces of silver.

Mary's love for Jesus was not just a private love. She was unashamed to fall at his feet and show her deep love and affection for Jesus. Are you ever embarrassed to share how much you love Jesus publically? If someone looked at how you spent your money this month, would they be able to tell that you love the Lord?

S—The S stands for *Scripture*

O—The O stands for *Observation*

A—The A stands for *Application*

K—The K stands for *Kneeling in Prayer*

By this all people will know

that you are my disciples,

if you have love for one another.

John 13:35

Reflection Question:

Jesus commanded the disciples not just to love their neighbor as themselves but rather he commanded them to love one another just as He loved them. This is a deep love. Jesus said that people would know we are his disciples by the way we deeply love each other.

Our love for each other is to be the mark of a believer's life. Non-christians should be able to identify us by our love for each other. How are you doing with loving your sisters in Christ? Is there a believer in your life that you are struggling to love well? Pray and ask the Lord to help you resolve any conflicts you have right now and ask God to give you His love for them. Write your prayer below and then take action on your prayer this week and show this person love.

John 13

S—The S stands for *Scripture*

O—The O stands for *Observation*

A—The A stands for *Application*

K—The K stands for *Kneeling in Prayer*

Peace I leave with you;

my peace I give to you.

Not as the world gives do I give to you.

Let not your hearts be troubled,

neither let them be afraid.

John 14:27

Reflection Question:

The world offers peace through many things such as money, big houses, fancy vacations, achievement, food, material pleasures, distractions, and even lies. But Jesus offers peace through the presence and power of the Holy Spirit.

The peace that Jesus gives does not include the absence of trouble. All of us will face many troubles in this world but Jesus offers us peace in the midst of our troubles. He is not the light at the end of the tunnel—He is the light IN the tunnel! What troubles are you facing today? How is Jesus your peace in the midst of your troubles?

S—The S stands for *Scripture*

O—The O stands for *Observation*

A—The A stands for *Application*

K—The K stands for *Kneeling in Prayer*

I am the vine:

you are the branches.

Whoever abides in me and I in him,

he it is that bears much fruit,

for apart from me you can do nothing.

John 15:5

Reflection Question:

A branch apart from the vine is dead. There is no life or fruit in a branch without the sap running through the vine to the branch. Not only are healthy branches fruitful but every piece of fruit has seeds inside that produce even more fruit. We should be the same!

God wants us to be fruitful and the only way we can do that is through remaining connected to Jesus. It's not that we can do nothing without God but rather that we can do nothing of *eternal value* without God. What fruit—of eternal value—do you see in your life from being connected to Jesus?

S—The S stands for *Scripture*

O—The O stands for *Observation*

A—The A stands for *Application*

K—The K stands for *Kneeling in Prayer*

In the world you will have tribulation.

But take heart;

I have overcome the world."

John 16:33

Reflection Question:

Jesus said his children will face struggles. We will not go from victory to victory without any valleys. But we should be encouraged, when we are in the midst of a valley, to know that Jesus is with us and has overcome the world.

Jesus did not tell us to cheer up or try harder, but rather to take heart, be encouraged and rest in His peace. Are you in a trial that has discouraged you? How does it help you to remember that Jesus is with you, loves you and has overcome this world?

John 16

S—The S stands for *Scripture*

O—The O stands for *Observation*

A—The A stands for *Application*

K—The K stands for *Kneeling in Prayer*

And this is eternal life,

that they know you,

the only true God,

and Jesus Christ whom you have sent.

John 17:3

Reflection Question:

Eternal life comes through knowing God and God manifested himself in bodily form through his son Jesus. We may know a lot of Bible verses and know a lot about God but that is different than knowing God personally. The unique thing about being a Christian is that it is more than just a religion, it is a genuine, intimate relationship with God!

It is such a blessing to not only know God personally but to also have the assurance of eternal life! Share below how you have personally experienced God in an intimate way in your life.

S—The S stands for *Scripture*

O—The O stands for *Observation*

A—The A stands for *Application*

K—The K stands for *Kneeling in Prayer*

When Jesus said to them, "I am he," they drew back and fell to the ground.

John 18:6

Reflection Question:

When Jesus declared "I am" the soldiers who came to arrest him realized they were not dealing with a normal man. This man had power and commanded authority. Jesus had the situation completely under his control and they were powerless to arrest him unless he allowed them to do so. All Jesus did was speak words and they were knocked to the ground!

Are you amazed at the power of your God? Jesus loves you so much that he willingly gave his life for you. How does this make you feel?

John 18

S—The S stands for *Scripture*

O—The O stands for *Observation*

A—The A stands for *Application*

K—The K stands for *Kneeling in Prayer*

Jesus said, "It is finished,"

and he bowed his head

and gave up his spirit.

John 19:30

Reflection Question:

When Jesus said "It is finished", this was not the cry of defeat but of triumph! Jesus had accomplished what he came to do. His work was complete and so he bowed his head in peace and willingly gave up his spirit.

Oh what a beautiful picture of his love for you and me! Jesus had authority over the soldiers and over his death but he willingly surrendered His life for us. Is there an area of your life that God is asking you to willingly surrender to Him? What is holding you back? Trust God today and fully surrender!

S—The S stands for *Scripture*

O—The O stands for *Observation*

A—The A stands for *Application*

K—The K stands for *Kneeling in Prayer*

*Blessed are those
who have not seen
and yet have believed.*

John 20:29

Reflection Question:

Thomas doubted. Thomas said he would never believe Jesus had risen unless he saw with his own eyes the mark of the nails and unless he could place his own hand, into his side.

Do you sometimes doubt God? Maybe you doubt he has truly forgiven you or you doubt that he has a good plan for you. Where does that doubt come from? What is the source of it? Pray and ask God to help you fight your doubts and overcome them. Trust God and His word today?

John 20

S—The S stands for *Scripture*

O—The O stands for *Observation*

A—The A stands for *Application*

K—The K stands for *Kneeling in Prayer*

Do you love me?

John 21:16

Reflection Question:

Peter had denied Jesus three times, so Jesus asked Peter three times, "Do you love me?"

Jesus is not looking for us to be good or do good deeds. He wants our heart. He wants our love and affection. Once he has our heart and all of our love—repentance and obedience will follow. Do you love Jesus? Tell him how much you love him today.

John 21

S—The S stands for *Scripture*

O—The O stands for *Observation*

A—The A stands for *Application*

K—The K stands for *Kneeling in Prayer*